Little
LAWMAKERS
: HOW TO TURN A BILL INTO A LAW

Women In Politics

10% of proceeds from this book will be donated to SheShouldRun

dedicated to
the women who came
before us

Table of Contents

"Nina, Nina, Nina! Look out the window! I think that's the Capitol building,"Ronin exclaimed as he pressed his face against the window of the school bus.

"Move over! Let me see," Nina replied excitedly, scooting closer to her best friend. A shiny white building with a wide base surrounded by columns, came into view. Nina was amazed. She had never seen such a distinct building.

Mr. Johansson, their teacher, laughed and turned to look at them from over his seat.

"Actually," he began addressing Nina and Ronin, "that's the Lincoln Memorial, not the Capitol building."

Mr. Johansson stood up in the bus aisle, facing the class, and pulled out tricolored flashcards from his right pocket. "All right, class, as we pass by each monument, I'll be providing you with some fun facts! First, on your right, is the Lincoln Memorial. It was built in honor of President Lincoln to symbolize the freedom and dignity of all people."

"Lincoln is my favorite president," whispered a boy in denim overalls to his friend.

"Oh yeah, that's the one with the funny beard and tall hat," a frizzy haired boy responded in a quiet voice.

"On your left is a building I'm sure you all will recognize," said Mr. Johansson, " can anyone name it?"

A wave of hands rose into the air. Nina stretched out her arm, almost jumping out of her seat, trying to catch Mr. Johansson's attention.

"Yes, Nina?"

"The White House!" Nina answered exuberantly.

"Yes, exactly correct," said Mr. Johansson with a smile.

"This is obviously where the President of the United States lives and works, but in fact, it wasn't called the White House until 1901 when it was named by

former President Theodore Roosevelt. Previously, it had been called the 'President's House' or 'President's Palace'. There are 132 rooms, with 32 bathrooms and six levels to accommodate all of the workers and visitors."

Mr. Johansson paused for a moment to catch his breath.

"Does anyone know how long a Presidential term is?"

Nina's hand is the only one that shot up. "Anyone else?" Mr. Johansson asks, trying to engage the rest of the class. While most of the students were staring blankly at their teacher, Ronin promptly decided to lift his arm.

"Four years!" Ronin exclaims.

Yes, very good, Ronin." he said reassuringly. "Alright everyone, now you will see a very tall building; the Washington Monument. Standing exactly 555 feet and 5 inches above the ground it was the tallest building in the world at the time. In 1887, that record was surpassed by the Eiffel Tower in Paris, France."

Mr. Johansson directs his attention back to the Washington Monument.

"If you look even closer, you can see the bricks change color, the lower third of the structure being a lighter shade of gray."

The kids pressed their faces up against the windows, eyes wide and chins raised.

"We'll be at the Capitol in 10 minutes." Mr. Johansson concluded.

Nina and Ronin perked up. It had been a long ride. The kids had been jostled at every bump and smooshed against one another at each turn.

Screech! The school bus grinded to another sudden halt, sending most of the students and their bags flying onto the floor covered with dried mud and crumbs. Cries of agitation echoed around the bus.

"Ouch!" yelled Ronin from his spot on the floor. Scrunching his face and rubbing his arm, he scrambled back up to the seat. "We almost just died!"

As he leaned back and threw a hand across his forehead, Nina retorted, "Oh, don't be so dramatic." Ronin was always one to exaggerate.

"No, look!" He shoved his arm in her face. "There's a bruise!"

"That's dirt," Nina said bluntly.

"Well, it still hurts," he said, crossing his arms with a pout.

Mr. Johansson got up and stood in the center of the aisle. "Is everyone okay?" he asked, looking around, "Those were some rough falls."

The students nodded hesitantly, Still struggling to get up.

"Wait Ronin, can you hand me my lunch box? It fell on the ground."

Ronin handed Nina her turquoise chevron-printed lunch box, an aroma drifting under his nose.

"Nina, what do you have for lunch? It smells so good!"

"My mom packed me my favorite Aji de Gallina dish."

"Isn't that the chicken chili with the milk sauce?"

"Yeah, it's a family recipe my grandmother taught my mom to make when we visited her in Peru last summer!" she said excitedly. Nina continued to dig through her lunch box, pulling out a can, "Oh! My mom also packed me Inca

Kola!" She cracked open the bottle and took a sip of the yellow, fruity soda before passing it to Ronin for him to try.

"It smells like bubblegum!" he exclaimed as he brought it to his mouth, flashing a mischievous grin.

"But it's not better than what I have for lunch."

"Ok, well then what do you have?" Nina inquired while giggling.

Ronin pulled his galaxy lunchbox onto his lap and unzipped it to reveal the Ramune soda and the onigiri rice balls his mom had packed for him.

"Awww those rice balls look like pandas! How did your mom make them?"

"My grandpa used to make them for my Mom everyday for lunch when she was in school in Japan!"

"Oh, and we both have sodas! Twins!" Nina exclaimed, gesturing towards his bottle of Ramune soda.

Before Ronin got a chance to show Nina the marble, Mr. Johansson interrupted them. He announced, "If you look to your right, you will see the Capitol Building!"

Nina and Ronin looked out the bus window. Glistening under the sun, the Capitol Building had a commanding presence with over 1.5

million square feet, towering columns, and hundreds of steps all crowned with the signature white dome - a symbol of the American government. The entire class stared in awe.

"This is a very important building where our laws are made," Mr. Johansson continued, "People from every state meet here to make these decisions for us and keep our country running. When we enter the building, we'll be taking a tour, so make sure to stay with the group and stick with your buddy." As the bus pulled up to the curb, the students filed off the bus energetically.

Nina and Ronin followed their classmates into the Capitol Building.

"Wow!" gasped Nina, stopping in her tracks. She looked up at the domed ceiling that rose above their heads, as painted angels sat triumphantly among soft, white clouds. Nina had never seen a more magnificent ceiling. She could not tear her eyes away. Each molded panel circled around and around, holding the painted eye of the ceiling high above her head. She nudged Ronin as she said, "Look up! It's so beautiful."

"That's called the Rotunda," a voice said from behind them. Nina, Ronin, and the rest of their class whirled around to see a tall person walking towards them. As the person stopped in front of them, they introduced themselves, saying, "Hello everyone! I'm your tour guide for the day. My name is Cameron, and I use he/him pronouns. I have been touring here for fifteen years, and I am so honored to witness the happenings of democracy every day. As a first-generation Belarussian American, I never thought I would have the opportunity to work here in the U.S Capitol. As your classmate pointed out, the Capitol has a gorgeous canopy featuring the Apotheosis of Washington painted in 1865. If you look closely, you will find that one of the angels is actually our first founding father, George Washington, on his way to heaven."

As Cameron continued to share the history behind the Rotunda, Nina noticed a woman dressed in a purple suit approaching them.

As she walked closer, Nina spotted a strangely patterned yellow, black, red, and white crab brooch pinned to the front of her suit.

She nudged Ronin, whispering, "Look at that lady's crab pin. Who do you think she is?"

"I don't know but she looks important," Ronin whispered back.

Smiling as she stopped in front of Nina and Ronin, the woman said, "Good morning, students! I am Congresswoman Ritah Akumu, representing the Third Congressional District in Maryland. I heard from Cameron here that you all are from my district too, so I wanted to stop by and welcome you to the Capitol. Since I have a meeting today that I need to prepare for, I can't stay and chat for too long, but I hope you enjoy your time here!"

A hand shot up and it was attached to a freckled-faced girl with red locks named Scarlett. Before the teacher could stop her, she blurted out, "I like your crab pin! Why does it have those colors?"

The Congresswoman laughed and replied, "Thank you! The blue crab is the Maryland state crustacean, which plays a big part in our state culture, and the colors are representative of the state flag. I wear it every day that I enter the Capitol."

"Alright class, let's wish Congresswoman Akumu good luck in her meeting," said Mr. Johansson, which was followed by a chorus of "byes" and "good lucks" from the students.

As the congresswoman waved goodbye and headed towards a decorated hallway, Cameron said, "Congresswoman Akumu is a representative in the House, which is only one part of Congress. The other part is the Senate, and together they write and pass our laws. Congresswoman Akumu heads the House Committee on Transportation and Infrastructure, which means that she's in charge of laws regarding buses and roads."

Whispers rose among the groups of students. "Do you think they mean our buses?" "Like the one we rode on today?" " That ride stinked!" "Yeah, remember when we all fell?"

Cameron attempted to re-engage the students' attention for the tour. "Now, if you would follow me, we are going to look at the Crypt."

3

As Cameron led the class down a flight of stairs, Ronin asked Nina excitedly, "Wait, a second! Do you think there are any mummies down there?"

Gripping the railing on the staircase, Nina giggled. "I think mummies are only in Egypt, so I hope not!"

Having overheard their conversation, Cameron interjected, "Well, there aren't any mummies down there, but there is a tomb..."

The rest of the students gasped. But Ronin, intrigued by this fact, blurted, "Is it haunted then?"

Scarlett stopped in her tracks. "If it's haunted, I'm not going down there!"

Cameron chuckled and said reassuringly, "Don't worry. No one's buried down there. The tomb was intended to be used for our first president, but old George Washington chose to be buried at his estate on Mount Vernon in 1799."

After making their way down the final steps, the group reached the lower floor where the Crypt was located. As they turned the corner, an arched hallway ending with a caged section revealed itself to them.

"I don't believe you," said Ronin as he stared down the hallway. "This place is definitely haunted." As they walked closer, the rusted edges of the locked gate

came into focus - its intimidating spires casting shadows onto the floor.
Approaching the gate, Cameron gestured toward the alcove containing a glossy,
black box.

"This is where George Washington would've been buried. Several decades
after his death, he was almost brought here again because in 1830 his actual
tomb in Mount Vernon was vandalized by grave robbers.

Congress was worried that his tomb wasn't secure enough. However, when
they tried to bring his body to the Capitol, where this other tomb in front of us
was located, the property owner at Mount Vernon decided to build Washington
a more secure tomb on the estate instead." Looking ahead into the well-lit
passageway, the group continued down the hallway.

"OoOoOo," whispered Ronin as he waved his arms in the air - his attempt at
imitating a ghost.

Scarlett ran to Mr. Johansson and clung to his arm. "I can hear the ghost!"
she cried. "I can feel it too; it's so cold in here."

Ronin and Nina couldn't hold in their laughter at this point, earning a frown
from Scarlett.

"Ronin!" chastised Mr. Johansson, shaking his head, but unable to hide a
smile.

Cameron suddenly stopped in his tracks and spun around to face the class.
Beside them stood a white marble statue of a stern-looking man crossing his
arms.

Cameron said, "Anne Whitney created this statue of Samuel Adams. Does
anyone know who that is?"

"Ooh! Ooh! I know!" Tyler pipes up, "Wasn't he a general in the American

"Yes!" Cameron exclaimed. "Samuel Adams was considered the 'Father of the American Revolution'. He's part of the reason why the U.S. is its own nation now!"

"Look Nina! I am Samuel Adams!" Ronin exclaimed while crossing his arms, mimicking the white marble statue that was towering above him.

The whole class erupted with laughter, as they all witnessed Ronin's shenanigans, which were solely intended for his best friend to see.

Stifling in a chuckle, Cameron exclaimed, "Yes, Ronin, you look just like him - just missing the wig!" Ronin blushed sheepishly as Cameron continued on.

SAMUEL ADAMS

"Samuel Adams was not only the Father of the Revolution, but also helped establish the Sons of Liberty, a group of Patriots who opposed British taxation. Tyler excitedly jumped up and exclaimed the motto "No Taxation, without Representation", as the whole class giggled remembering Mr. Johansson's lesson. "Exactly!" Cameron responded with a smile. "Now, if you follow me, we're going to go further into the Crypt." Every state gives the Capitol two statues. This one is from Massachusetts."

As they walk past various statues, Ronin stops and tugs on Nina's sleeve, pulling her to a stop as well. Pointing at the dulled bronze statue in front of him, he announces, "Look, Nina! This is a statue from Maryland. That's our state!"

"This statue is of Charles Carroll, Maryland's first statesman and a signer of the Declaration of Independence," Cameron pointed out.

Nina looked down and gasped, "Look at his gold shoes! They're so shiny!"

"Yeah, I want shoes like that!" says Ronin.

"Did you know that bronze statues turn golden when rubbed?" asks Cameron.

"No way!" says Nina as she reaches over to rub the shoes, followed by Ronin.

"Let's go see if there is another statue from Maryland!" Ronin started walking group unnoticed. Nina followed closely behind as they headed in a new direction. They walked in circles throughout the Crypt, weaving around columns and checking the state labels on each statue they passed.

Noticing a staircase ahead, Ronin said, "I don't think there is another statue here. Let's go upstairs!"

Nina stopped and hesitated for a moment, saying, "But Ronin, we don't know where that goes.

"It'll be fine, I promise. I remember seeing statues before we came down anyway. We'll be super quick!"

Nina sighed and followed Ronin up the stairs reluctantly.

They emerged in the Rotunda full of excited tourists. They tried to walk towards some statues but got caught up in a wave of people. The crowd jostled Nina and Ronin, pulling them along. At last, the people began to disperse. Nina and Ronin caught their breath and looked around the unfamiliar room. Large paintings hung on the walls. There wasn't a single statue in sight.

"Ronin, where are we?" Nina asked nervously. "Where's Cameron? Where's our class?"

Ronin walked to the doorway and looked down the hall, hoping to see something familiar. He turns back to Nina with wide eyes. "I think we're lost..."

"No, no! We can't be lost," Nina panicked, shaking her head. "I told you we should have stayed downstairs. Now what are we going to do!" she said, turning to face Ronin, her eyes wide with panic.

"Oh it's fine! We'll find the group soon," Ronin replied. Nina began to pace nervously around the now empty room, her shoes clicking against the tiled floor. Her mind raced trying to figure out how they were going to find their way back to their classmates.

Her heart was beating so fast it felt like it was going to burst out of her chest.

Ronin observed Nina's anxious state, and he could feel himself begin to panic about the situation too. Despite this, Ronin turned to the most comforting thing he knew, and, lifting his arm, he began to armpit fart.

Nina did her best to look annoyed and stifle a snort. "What was that for?!" she demanded.

Ronin shrugged, "What? It calms me down? Aren't you feeling calmer now?"

"Actually, a little," Nina giggled.

"Well, good! Why don't we look in the hall and find someone to help us?"

Nina took a deep breath and nodded, "Good idea."

"This looks a lot like the ceiling of the big Rotunda!" Nina said.

Ronin ran to the center of the room and clung to the railing wrapped around an opening in the ground. "Nina, come look! You can see the bottom floor, where we just were! Maybe our class is still down there."

Nina rushed over in hopes that this messy situation would soon be over and peered over the railing. The two of them watched and waited but they couldn't see any of their classmates or Mr. Johanssen. Ronin pulled his head back, "I don't think they're down there. Let's go look somewhere else."

"Ronin, it's only been thirty seconds. You have the attention span of a goldfish!"

"Ok fine," Ronin said with a huff, "let's look a little longer."

They looked for their class over the railing a little bit longer. Both noticed the white marble statues from earlier, but no person in sight. "Okay, now we can look somewhere else," Nina said. "I don't think they're coming."

"Who has a short attention span now!" Ronin laughed.

As Nina and Ronin stepped away from the railing, Ronin noticed another door nearby. "Let's go through there!" he said to Nina.

Nina followed him through the door. This time they found themselves in a large semi-circular room. Nina's stomach dropped. "I don't think we should be in here Ronin; this looks really official" she said, pausing in the doorway. Ronin didn't listen to her and scurried around the room, sitting at the various mahogany desks that lined the room. "I bet this is where the politicians sit when they make the laws!"

"Which is exactly why we need to leave!" Nina whisper-shouted, pointing to the large wooden doors they had just entered through.

Ronin ignored her and turned his head to the front of the room, letting out a gasp.

There, beneath red velvet drapes, sat the largest mahogany desk of all and behind it, a majestic red leather chair. Ronin ran across the carpeted floor and jumped into the big leather seat below a painting of George Washington. "Nina, look at me! I am royalty! Come bow before me, my loyal subject."

Nina laughed and walked down to stand in front of Ronin, "Don't let the power get to your head, your royal highness."

Ronin scooched over in the chair as Nina walked around the desk and sat next to him. They looked out over the chamber. "You're right, I do feel like royalty."

As Nina and Ronin sat surveying their empty kingdom, they heard the sound of running heels going click clack click clack down the hall.

Nina immediately perked up, remembering that they probably weren't supposed to be in this mystery room. Looking through the door, they saw a woman rush past in a blur of purple followed by a subtle clink.

"I think that was Congresswoman Akumu!" Nina exclaimed. "I recognized her purple suit."

"Anyone could be wearing a purple suit," Ronin said. "How do you know it was her?"

"Let's go check," Nina said, jumping out of the seat and hurrying to the door. They walked into the hall and noticed an object on the tile.

"Look, there's something sparkly on the floor!" Ronin said.

Nina knelt down and picked it up, "It's her crab brooch!"

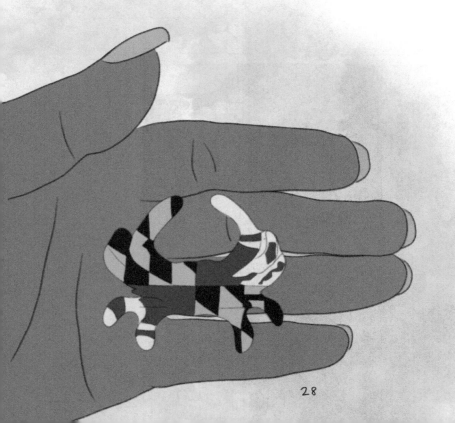

"**Didn't Congresswoman Akumu say** that this pin was really meaningful to her?" Ronin asked.

"Yeah, maybe we should give it back to her!" Nina responded.

"Ok yeah, but we need to hurry because she's leaving right now!" Ronin said, pointing in the direction of her fastly disappearing purple figure.

"Oh, right, she has that meeting! We need to get it to her before it starts!"

"Then let's go right now!" Ronin said while chasing after Congresswoman Akumu, motioning for Nina to do the same.

Nina and Ronin darted after her down the extended hallway, making a right turn where they last saw Congresswoman Akumu. They saw a splash of purple scurrying across the marble floor as they rounded the corner, entering the Rotunda.

"Oh we've been here before! Look Ronin, it's George Washington again!" Nina observed.

"Wow that dude is everywhere!" Ronin retorted.

Before they had a chance to fully take in their surroundings, they noticed the purple suited congresswoman make another turn leaving the Rotunda.

"Look there she is! She's turning again - let's hurry!" Nina said in between breaths. Ronin, huffing in response, followed his friend through the crowd ahead. The Rotunda began to fill up as a new group of tourists shuffled in behind their guide, making it difficult to navigate. Nina wriggled her way through the towering adults trying to find her way through the maze of legs. Nina turned back to check on her friend only to see him sandwiched between a tall, skirted woman and a corduroy-panted man.

"Keep going, Ronin!" Nina yelled through the crowd.

"Go on without me or you'll never catch up to her! I'll only hold you back!" Ronin cried out in the most theatrical manner.

Nina laughed and said, "No man left behind!"

Nina took a breath and threw herself back into the swarming crowd, pushing her way through, determined to rescue Ronin.

"Here, grab my hand!" Nina said, reaching out.

Ronin extended his arm, but his fingers could barely reach Nina's.

After they stretched their arms the farthest they could go, his fingers finally latched onto hers. Nina led the way out ducking under, around, and in-between the moving crowd. When they finally got out, both of them let out a sigh of relief.

"Thanks, Nina. I never thought I would make it out of there alive. I was about to be trampled." Ronin said dramatically as he looked at Nina in awe. "You're my hero!"

She laughed and said, "That's just what friends do for each other! Let's keep going though. We should see if Congresswoman Akumu is somewhere in the next hallway."

Ronin regained his breath, as he followed Nina around the corner where they last saw the Congresswoman. They entered a quiet corridor with muffled sounds behind closed doors.

"She might be in one of these rooms," Ronin said.

They walked down the passage slowly, hearing voices from each room.

The first door that appeared was labeled "Foreign Affairs Subcommittee".

"We should try to find the one that says 'Transportation'" Nina said. "That's her committee, right?"

"I'm 94% sure that's it," Ronin replied.

As they got closer to the 'Foreign Affairs' door, the faint voices from within became more passionate. Out of curiosity, Nina and Ronin leaned in to listen.

"...We should allocate funding to health care in underdeveloped countries. It's part of the duty of the United States as a wealthy country" a deep voice exclaimed.

"Funding is not enough. These countries need more hands-on assistance that we are capable of providing! We should create more programs that encourage our medical professionals to take time working overseas." a lady strongly rebutted.

"But would it be too invasive to send over our own people? I believe that sending over advanced medical equipment is sufficient because..." a southern-accented voice interjected as it faded out.

"They sound like they're going to be arguing for hours!" said Nina.

"If you think that one is interesting, you should come over here and listen to this one!" Ronin said, gesturing for her to come over.

They pressed their ears to another door, this time labeled, "Committee on Science, Space, and Technology."

A static commentator suddenly shouted, "Perseverance has made contact with Mars at 13:02 pm!"

Cheers erupted in the room, making

so much noise that Nina and Ronin had to move away from the door.

"YES! This is great news for the future of our space program and the expedition to Mars!"

A gentle sounding voice added, "And the rover is so cute!"

"Ooo that's so cool! Could you imagine if they found actual aliens on Mars?" Ronin exclaimed to Nina.

But Nina was only half listening though; her attention had been stolen by the voices coming from a door labeled 'Committee on Agriculture'. Nina pressed her ear against the door as a voice said,

I am worried about how low-income communities are going to get healthier food options especially during the current food insecurity crisis.

A representative with a southern accent piped up, "I am very concerned as well. My constituents in Louisiana are not receiving the food they need. We have one of the largest food deserts in the country that needs to be addressed."

"Maybe we could create a government program, modeled after companies like Misfit Market or Imperfect Foods*" a soft voice explained.

"C'mon Nina we don't have time to listen to them any longer. We need to look for the 'Transportation Committee' room, so we can give Congresswoman Akumu her brooch back!"

"Yeah you're right we gotta hurry."

Coming out of one room labeled 'Committee on Homeland Security,' a voice passionately argued, *"I think we are focusing too many resources on international terrorist threats, and not enough on domestic threats. Some of the greatest dangers to the nation reside right here on our soil..."*

Another set of convincing voices, from the 'Committee on the Climate Crisis' room, infiltrated Ronin and Nina's ears: *"We need to implement policies that support our 'CLEAN Future Act' if we really want to achieve greenhouse gas emission net zero by 2050."*

"Wow, there's a lot of debates going on along this hallway," Ronin commented.

"I know, but none of them are about transportation. Where in the world is Congresswoman Akumu?"

Ronin and Nina began to grow worried. They wanted to find Congresswoman Akumu to give her crab brooch back, but they were running out of time before their class left the Capitol.

"It's ok Nina, maybe if we keep walking we will find the Committee on Transportation room with Congresswoman Akumu," Ronin reassured Nina, who was pacing uneasily again. Nina nodded her head, feeling grateful to be lost with her calm best friend. Ronin led the way down the hallway past several doors, peering into each carefully, when suddenly Nina caught a glimmer of purple.

"Wait Ronin, come here really quickly. I think I saw something!" Ronin speed walked back to where Nina stood with one eye squinting through a sliver of a cracked door.

"That's her, Ronin, that's her!"

"Wait, really? Step aside, let me see."

Before Ronin got a chance to peek for himself, the mahogany door shut in his face, centimeters away from hitting his nose. Ronin's jaw dropped with shock as he took a step back, looking for his best friend's reaction. Nina's face looked stunned, staring at the door with disbelief.

Their momentary astonishment was interrupted by Nina thinking out loud, "What should we do now? How are we going to give her the brooch back?"

"Are you even sure that it was Congresswoman Akumu?" Ronin asked.

"Yes, Ronin. I pinky swear that it was her! If you don't believe me, just listen through the door. Maybe we can hear her voice."

The two best friends pressed their ears lightly against the towering door. They began to pick up the sounds of disgruntled, muffled voices. "…yes, some states already have their own regulations, let's just leave it to them. Nationally mandated seat belts for school buses would be an overreach of federal power. "

"An overreach of power? We would single handedly save children's lives and protect their safety. In this case the federal government is using their power for good!"

"Do we even need seatbelts on school buses though? We have gone so long without them, and the kids seem fine…"

"…yeah what does the public demand even look like for this issue…none of my constituents have written to me about it…"

Nina lifted her head off the door, her eyes widening as she looked at Ronin.

"They are talking about school bus seat belts, Ronin! Remember how you bruised your elbow on the ride here?"

"Oh yeahhhh," Ronin began to rub his mildly bruised elbow, "it still kinda hurts!"

"Well maybe we should tell the Congress people that you got hurt, and they will want to pass the seatbelt legislation!"

"I don't know Nina, we should probably stick to just returning Congresswoman Akumu's crab brooch. I mean that's why we started on this adventure in the first place."

Nina thought for a second. Ronin did have a point, and she usually liked to stick to the plan, but something about the committee's conversation compelled her to want to take action.

"Maybe you're right, but I think we could actually help the committee reach a decision. Let's listen a little bit longer before we decide how we are going to return the brooch."

Nina and Ronin pressed their ears back up against the door, waiting in suspense for more shouting.

They heard Congresswoman Akumu's distinct voice float through the heavy door. "I think both arguments are valid, but ultimately we need to hear from the people that the policy directly affects. Do we want to get in touch with some public school students?"

"*Pfft* what do students know about federal policy or care about school bus safety? They are just kids."

Just kids? Nina thought indignantly, *JUST KIDS? What did he mean "just kids"?*

Before Nina could process what she was doing, she reached up and grabbed the door handle, shoving it open with the weight of her full body. She burst into the committee room, dragging a surprised Ronin behind her, while a room full of incredulous Congress people stared at the two best friends in astonishment.

Nina and Ronin found themselves facing down a group of well-dressed representatives gathered around a large oval table. Among the large group there were many individuals: a red-haired man dressed in navy; a grey pants-suited woman with olive skin; and the signature purple suit of Congresswoman Akumu.

Upon seeing the children burst into their meeting, the adults in the room paused mid debate.

Congresswoman Akumu locked eyes with Nina and shot up out of her seat. "Hello, can I help you? Are you two lost?" she inquired with concern, approaching them.

"Um…uh…we just…," Nina stuttered, suddenly losing her train of thought as she gazed into the sea of startled eyes. Her brain seemed to know all the words she wanted to say, but her voice was unwillingly stuck in her throat. She nudges Ronin, signaling for support.

"I think what my friend is trying to say…is that WE ALMOST DIED!"

A low mumbling occurred throughout the room, the adults seemed even more confused now.

"Oh! Is everything ok?" Congresswoman Akumu asked compassionately.

"Yeah like earlier today we were on our school bus and suddenly we heard a 'Screeeeeeeeech' as the bus driver slammed on the brakes and then BAM! I was on the ground with dirt all in my mouth…Nina and I compared sodas and lunches… ghosts haunted us in the crypt… we saw statues of dead people, a weird shaped room, and almost got trampled by a huge stampede. By the way, your purple dress was very helpful --"

"Well it sounds like you've had an eventful day. Do you need help finding your class?"

"No. Well, not yet!" Nina cut in, finding her voice. "We got separated from our class during the tour and as we were trying to find our way back we saw you! We were going to ask you for help but you looked like you were in a hurry and you dropped your brooch, which we recognized from earlier, and we wanted to return it to you so we followed you here!"

"Well that's awfully sweet of you, but you should really be getting back to your class," Congresswoman Akumu said in a gentle but firm voice. She began to usher the two kids out while motioning to some younger people in the crowd to help them find their class. Nina and Ronin were carefully nudged over to the door, between the Congresswoman and her helpers. The two students began to panic as they realized that their opinions on school bus safety would not be heard. In one last act of determination - as they were halfway through the door - Nina urged, "Wait! Please just listen to what we have to say!"

"Say about what?" Congresswoman Akumu said curiously.

"Seat belts in school buses. We have personal experience," Nina said as she pointed to Ronin's elbow. Ronin theatrically lifted his arm, flourishing his bruise.

"See! I told you we almost died!"

"…and this was all because you didn't have…seatbelts?" A congressman piped up in the background.

"Yes, actually, when the bus suddenly came to a hard stop, my friend Ronin here fell forward on the ground and hurt his elbow. I think this wouldn't have happened if there would've been seatbelts on the bus," Nina declared.

"This is exactly what I was saying," Congresswoman Akumu said while turning back to face her colleagues, "This is an actual public school student, sharing her experiences. And what she is saying, is that we need seatbelts on buses to protect children."

"I mean, I agree, but it's a matter of execution. Can we afford it?" said a congressman in the back.

The congregation was silent for one second, and then suddenly all erupted in overlapping arguments.

"I just don't know how essential seat belts are to school buses…"

"Yeah, it's never been a problem in the past until now…"

"I mean that kid did get hurt…"

Then, out of all of the shouting, Ronin heard one Congressman say, "Well it's just a bruise it could've been worse…"

He gasped in offense, "Just a bruise! JUST A BRUISE! Do you see the color of my elbow! It's amazing I have survived all of my years without a seatbelt!"

Nina was overwhelmed by all of the arguing. She had to do something to make sure this policy passed. Nina looked around and jumped up onto the nearest chair and yelled "EVERYONE PLEASE STOP YELLING!"

Everyone stopped in their tracks and craned their necks to look towards the audacious little girl who was scolding a room full of government officials. Ronin looked up, beaming with pride for his best friend.

   "I know I am just a kid, but please hear me out. Us kids care about a bunch of issues, not just seat belt safety...um...like as we were walking here, and Ronin and I heard people arguing about climate change... and uh we care about that too because it's our generation's future and this is the planet we will live on and take care of after you all are gone...also with uh.. With immigration! Ronin and I know about immigration because we both come from immigrant families, so we know there are less fortunate people in the world that could use our resources and help. We know and care more about the world than grown-ups think we do...so...that's why our voices matter, especially when it comes to seatbelts! It may cost more, but I think our lives are worth more than the cost. We are the ones riding the buses, so
if we feel unsafe, it is your responsibility as leaders of our nation to make us feel safer.

The entire room was too stunned to blink an eye.

Ronin interrupted the deafening silence by jumping up on the chair next to Nina's and pumping his fist in the air, saying, "What she said!"

Smiles spread across the congress people's faces.

"Well, thank you Nina. And Ronin, of course," Congresswoman Akumu said, looking proud of the students for confidently voicing their opinions. "I certainly agree that the issues we, as representatives discuss, affect everyone. Therefore, it's important that we listen to kids as well as adults." She nodded her head and continued, "I agree that you're the ones riding the buses and being impacted by this issue so for that reason, I vote 'aye' on this proposal." Congresswoman Akumu raised her hand as she sat back down, signaling her vote. "All those in favor?"

There was a chorus of "ayes" as all but one person raised their hand.

Waiting for his response, all eyes were glued to the last person, Congressman Richards, as he sat unmoving, with his hand firmly by his side. Congressman Richards sighed and said, "Before this meeting, I was planning on voting 'nay' because I was concerned about the complicated financial burden of this proposal. But, after hearing from young students who are so passionate about this matter it really makes my decision quite simple. I vote 'aye'." Congressman Richards raised his hand in favor, and the room erupted in joyful cheers and clapping.

8

As the Congress people filed out of the room, they high-fived Ronin and Nina who looked over at each other with large grins on their faces.

"That was so cool! I can't believe they actually listened to us!" Nina exclaimed, jumping up and down giddily.

"Yeah, that was pretty cool, but why did we need to convince them in the first place? Why couldn't we have just gone ahead and passed this bill without their votes since we know seatbelts would be a good thing for our community?" Ronin turned to Congresswoman Akumu, looking at her quizzically.

"That's a great question, Ronin! Typically, we like to include everyone in the decision-making process, even if we do not technically need their vote to pass the proposal. We are all working together on this piece of legislation, so it's important that we hear each other's opinions and listen to others' experiences. That's how we learn from each other and how we can best serve our constituents.

"Ohhh, I get it," Nina said. "Like how at school, we work together on group projects and have to make sure everyone is included."

"Yeah! Just like that! Teamwork is everywhere."

"But wait, what if nobody can agree and no one is willing to work together?

What happens then?" Ronin questioned.

"Ah, that's where bipartisanship comes in. In the United States, we primarily have a two-party system, meaning two prominent parties - the Democratic and Republican - dominate our governing process. When members of these two groups clash on issues, such as the seatbelt law, we have to find a way to compromise or nothing would get done. "

"Ok, that makes sense. So, now that our seatbelt proposal has passed, what happens next? Are we going to get seat belts in our buses?" Nina asked.

"Well, it's not that simple. Now that the Transportation Committee has passed this specific proposal, other committees have to look it over and modify the details." Congresswoman Akumu explained.

"Wait a second, you're telling me that wasn't the end?" Ronin asked in shock. "There's more???"

Congresswoman Akumu chuckled, "Yup, there's more! Next, we have to send it to the Appropriations Committee, so they can approve the money allotted for the bill. After they approve our proposal, we have to schedule a vote, where all the members of the House of Representatives come to vote yay, nay, or abstain. To pass the bill, we need a majority of votes in favor. Then, we send it to the Senate..."

"What happens in the Senate?" Nina asked, eagerly.

"Well, the Senate conducts a similar process to the House. They also debate over the details of the bill in committees, and bring it to the Senate floor for a vote. It's a long process because if anything changes in the bill, both chambers of Congress have to approve it again," Congresswoman Akumu paused, noticing the kids' widened, overwhelmed eyes. "The process is almost done, I promise!" Nina and Ronin smile and nod reassuringly.

"Phew, thank goodness! I was worried it was going to take forever to make a law." Ronin said, wiping a hand across his forehead.

Congresswoman Akumu laughed, "Not forever, Ronin, but it is a little long. After Congress passes the bill, it ends up on the desk of the President of the United States to sign it into law!"

What if the president doesn't want to sign it?" Ronin questioned.

"The President has the power to veto a bill, meaning that it has to go back to Congress. If they choose to, Congress can go through the whole process again and make changes to appease the president."

"That sounds like a lot of work to redo to me!" Nina said matter-of-factly. "I don't know if I would be up for that."

"You'd be surprised, but a lot of congress people aren't up for that either, which is why many bills fail after a presidential veto."

Does that mean they can just veto any bill and it automatically stops there?" Ronin asked, surprised.

"Actually, the president doesn't always have the final say! If Congress comes together, they can override the veto."

"So teamwork really does make the dream work, huh?" Ronin winked towards Nina and Congresswoman Akumu, who were both clutching their stomachs and laughing at Ronin's silliness.

"Yes, exactly Ronin -- wait. You two have been away from your tour and classmates for awhile now, I need to get you back to your teacher!"

Ronin and Nina sighed and looked at each other, realizing their adventure was coming to an end.

"I guess we should return," replied Nina reluctantly. As she tugged at her best friend to follow her out the door, Ronin realized they had one more thing to do. He reached in his pocket and pulled out what got them there in the first place.

"Before we go, here's your crab brooch that you dropped earlier!"

"Oh, thank you! Like I said to your class, this has a lot of sentimental value to me as a Maryland Congresswoman. As a token of my appreciation, would you two enjoy a tour on our way back to your class?"

"Yes! Yes! Yes!" shouted Nina and Ronin in unison. And with that, the three of them left the committee room and headed down the hallway cheerily.

9

Congresswoman Akumu led the group down the stairs into the Crypt.

Ronin exclaimed, "We've already been here! We saw George Washington's tomb and heard the sounds of his ghost!"

"Is that so?" Congresswoman Akumu replied with a laugh. "Well in that case, I'll show you something more interesting."

The Congresswoman turned around and proceeded to move through a maze of turns through twisted corridors that finally opened up into a grand hall lined with aged marble columns. The kids slowed their pace, taking in the architectural beauty before them. The hallway was narrow, but the ceilings were high and lined with embellished blocks that ran all the way down the long hall. To either side of them were bronze and marble statues of men, whose eyes seemed to follow their steps.

"This is the Hall of Columns, where part of the National Statuary Hall Collection is housed." Congresswoman Akumu said.

"Maybe the other Maryland statute is somewhere here!" Nina said excitedly to Ronin. She turned to address Congresswoman Akumu, "We saw the other one earlier in the Crypt and we've been trying to find the second one all day."

Congresswoman Akumu smiled. "Then you can stop searching because the second statue, of John Hanson, is riiiiiiight here." She stopped in front of a bronze man on a marble pedestal labeled 'Maryland'.

The kids stopped beside her to take in the statue's thoughtful expression.

"This statue was given to the Collection by the state of Maryland in 1903. Mr. Hanson was a very accomplished man who, as a member of the Continental Congress, facilitated the ratification of the Articles of Confederation, and then went on to help America gain a position on the world stage as a member of Congress."

"I remember reading about the Articles of Confederation in history class. The Articles didn't last very long because the government was too weak and it eventually led to the creation of the U.S. Constitution, which is what we still use today." Nina added, proud of herself for remembering.

"Very good, Nina!" The Congresswoman replied with a smile and a twinkling thought in her eye.

"Oh! And the funny hat he's wearing is shaped like a triangle, called a tri-corner hat! They were super popular back in colonial days!" Ronin added, also wanting to impress Congresswoman Akumu.

"That's very good Ronin! I can tell both of you pay great attention in class!" Congresswoman Akumu said.

The group walked the remaining length of the hall, made a turn, and went up a different set of stairs. After a few paces they entered a grand room, lined with seats in a semicircle, around three main desks at the front of the room that stood in front of the American flag.

"Now this is my favorite room in the entire Capitol Building. This is where the magic happens. Welcome to the House Chamber."

Nina and Ronin froze in amazement as they tried to take in the intricacies of the room. Everything seemed so official: the vibrant blue carpet with the circular yellow emblems, the regal clock on the wall surrounded by eagles and cornucopias carved out of gold, and black marble ionic columns on either side of the American flag. Noticing their astonishment, Congresswoman Akumu smiled to herself, remembering the feeling of standing in such an elegant, dignified space for the first time.

"This very chamber you are standing in was first entered by representatives in 1857," Congresswoman Akumu informed Nina and Ronin, sensing their desire for more information.

Ronin and Nina kept swiveling their heads around, slowly taking in every moment, knowing they would miss it later on the bus.

Almost as if a force was pulling him towards the center of the chamber, Ronin began to wander astray from where they had entered the room.

"Can we sit in the big fancy chair up there Congresswoman?" Ronin inquired, pointing to the biggest chair at the highest desk in the center of the room.

With reluctance Congresswoman Akhumu explains, "Oh I wish you could, but that spot is reserved for the Speaker of the House, so we should probably get going. Maybe one day you will get to sit in that chair as a Representative yourself!"

"Ooo maybe!," Ronin said excitedly, suddenly delighted by the idea.

Congresswoman Akumu proposed that they continue down the hall to get back to their class.

As they made their way through the building, Nina observed a set of double doors. She stopped, sensing that there was something different about this section. She turned to get a closer look and saw a plaque above the door labeled "Speaker's Lobby." Ronin followed her gaze.

"Who is a speaker? Ronin asked.

"It's actually the Speaker," Congresswoman Akumu answered. "The full title is Speaker of the House of Representatives. They are a representative that leads House proceedings."

Ronin interrupted with a "Huh?", looking to his friend for clarification.

"It's like the team leader for a group project in class. You select that person as a group and then they are responsible for leading discussion and expressing our collective thoughts to the rest of the class," Nina explained eagerly.

"Exactly, Nina," Congresswoman Akumu smiled.

She continued proudly, "They are the highest ranking member of the House of Representatives. Our Speaker is a great woman, and a mentor of mine." After a moment, she looked down at her watch. "Oh goodness, look at the time! We really need to find your class."

Nina glanced back to take one more look at the plaque before they moved on.

Upon their re-entrance into the Rotunda, Nina and Ronin noticed that it had been busier than when they first arrived in the morning. There was an echoing buzz of voices around the room and swirling groups of people moving with purpose.

"Do you see your class anywhere?" Congresswoman Akumu's voice sounded clear as it cut through the background chatter.

The kids looked around the room before Ronin answered, "I can't see them, but they should be in here. We were supposed to finish the tour back in the Rotunda at 2:30. It's 2:28 now." He frowned.

A flutter of panic entered Nina's stomach as she anxiously wondered if they somehow missed their class. She had enjoyed their Capitol adventure, but she didn't want to be stuck here forever, or even worse, get in trouble with Mr. Johansson.

While Nina was frantically searching for a trace of their class, Ronin stepped up onto the nearest bench, trying to gain a higher point of view over the congregation of bodies. After gaining an extra three feet of height, Ronin was able to get a clearer view to search for a distinguishable sign of their class.

"Ronin, do you see anyone? Mr. Johansson? Anything at all???" Nina asked urgently. "Do you think they would leave without us?"

Ronin, who was still scanning the room, felt discouraged by the absence of any sign of their class. Just as he began to step down off the bench, panic building, his eye caught a glimpse of bright red hair. It was Scarlett!

"Nina! Nina! Nina! Red hair! Scarlett! It's her! She must be with our class!" Ronin announced, jumping up and down on the creaking bench.

"Careful Ronin! Don't break the bench or else we will have to take you to the Supreme Court," Congresswoman Akumu said with a humorous undertone.

"Wait, Ronin, are you sure it's them? Like 100% sure?" Nina inquired, craning her neck to look towards her towering best friend.

"Yes I am 343% sure! It was her, I swear! Unless she's lost too…"

"Let me see!," Nina said as she took a large step onto the bench, almost pushing Ronin off. "How can you see anything better up here?"

"You two be careful up there, I can't have *two* hurt children under my watch," the Congresswoman warned cautiously with a warm smile.

"Oh wait! I see her! The red hair! It's right there!" Nina exclaimed, matching Ronin's excitement.

"See, I told you! Let's go," Ronin says, taking Nina's hand so they don't get separated in the sea of people.

"Wait you two, not just yet," Congresswoman Akumu interjected, "Come here, there's something I want to show you before you head off."

The Congresswoman took off the red and yellow patterned crab brooch that she had dropped earlier.

"Remember this crab pin you returned to me? It was actually given to me by a very kind constituent a couple months after I was elected. I was new to politics and was starting to doubt that I would ever accomplish anything meaningful, but when she sent me this little token, it reminded me that my number one job was to advocate for my community. They are the people that inspire my work everyday. Even though you aren't my constituent yet, thinking of creating a brighter future for kids like you keeps me going. You reminded me to advocate today in that committee room, and reach across the aisle for solutions. Your passion was greater than any ideological differences and we were able to reach a bipartisanship agreement. I fought for the safety of my district today and for that I want to thank you."

Nina and Ronin followed her every word with thoughtful consideration.

Congresswoman Akumu continued as she took off her crab brooch, "So, now, I am passing this to you, Nina, so you can also remember to be accepting of others even if their opinions are different from yours. I can see the same ambition and compassion for politics and governing that I had when I was younger, in you. I hope that one day you will represent Maryland's Third District with pride. I will be there to cheer you on."

Congresswoman Akumu kneeled down and gently placed the brooch in the small hands before her, cupping Nina's hands in her own before softly releasing them. Nina grinned widely, looking down at the brooch in her hands as if it were the key to unlocking some undiscovered magic within herself.

"Thank-- thank you so much Congresswoman Akumu." Nina said, simply stunned at her generosity and faith in her. Her eyes were wide as she blinked incredulously. "This is so amazing! I hope I can become a great person like you one day!" Nina ran in to embrace the Congresswoman tightly. Congresswoman Akumu turned to Ronin now with a smile.

"And for you Ronin, I have something special too," Congresswoman Akumu said while pulling a fancy gold pen out of her suit jacket.

"Every Congress person is given a few official Congressional pens when we are elected. They have the official Congressional seal on them and our name. These are definitely not the ones sold in the gift shop. This one of a kind pen is for a truly one of a kind little man like you, Ronin." She said 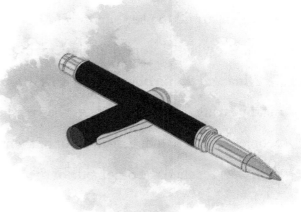 proudly, placing the pen into Ronin's eager hands.

"Whoa, it's so heavy! What is this made of, pure gold?" Ronin asked.

Congresswoman Akumu chuckled, "No, but it sure feels like it, huh!"

Congresswoman Akumu chuckled, "No, but it sure feels like it, huh!"

Nina and Ronin turned towards each other, admiring one another's new gifts. The Congresswoman stood up and beamed with delight.

After a few moments of Nina and Ronin marveling at their new tokens, the Congresswoman chided, "Now go meet up with the rest of your class!"

"Thank you Congresswoman for taking care of us today and helping us find our way back. You are my role model and I will never forget today!" Nina said while running to the Congresswoman for a hug.

"Yeah, you're totally awesome!" Ronin added.

"No, thank YOU two for being awesome. You inspired me today. Both of you reminded me and many other people in the committee room to be accepting and listen to different sides of an issue. Your experience on that school bus played a big role in the legislative process today."

Both of them smiled.

Congresswoman Akumu looked at both of them one last time and said, "Never be afraid to use your voice. After all, it is YOUR future." She winked at them. "Now, go! Before your class really leaves without you!"

Nina and Ronin obliged and waved goodbye before turning around and disappearing into the crowd. As they made their way through the Rotunda, the people seemed to disperse in front of them like clouds parting for the sun. Very soon they reached the other side of the room, just as Mr. Johansson was doing the final roll call.

"...Scarlett?" Mr. Johansson spoke to the group.

"Here" The red-headed girl chirped in reply.

"Ronin?"

"Present!" Ronin said victoriously and slightly panting.

"Nina?"

"Here!" Nina said with a major sigh of relief, and immediately added in a whisper to Ronin "We were almost *not* here."

"Tyler…. Sam… Marietta…" He continued, with each student responding.

Nina and Ronin's mouths stayed quiet, although their eyes were both speaking to each other playfully.

When Mr. Johansson finished calling all of the names, the class began to walk through the front doors in which they had entered just hours before. They made their way back to the bus, both of them silently saying a goodbye to all the wonders of the Capitol and the adventure they had. Climbing the stairs of the bus and making their way back to their seats, Nina and Ronin rediscovered the lunches they had left behind.

"I just realized how hungry I am," Ronin said, reaching down to grab his lunchbox.

"Me too," Nina added.

They grabbed their lunch bags and unzipped them, both reaching for their drinks first. Not a word was said between them as they looked at each other, with drinks in hand, and clinked their glasses together in harmony. After taking a sip, they sunk into their seats as the exhaustion from the day finally hit them. They ate their food peacefully staring out the window at all the different monuments they passed. The bus still shook and swayed with every bump and turn, but this time for Nina and Ronin it felt different. They savored each jump and jostle because they hoped that soon there would be seatbelts on buses and it would all be because of their efforts today.

Ronin grabbed a notebook out of his bag and began journaling and doodling his experiences from the day, with his shiny gold pen, trying not to forget even the tiniest detail. Nina wistfully drifted off into a light sleep and dreamed about herself in a tailored purple suit, proudly sporting her Maryland crab brooch while speaking on the House of Representatives chamber floor. As if the universe wanted to celebrate their achievements that day, the sky was painted in pastel hues as the bus drove off into the sunset.

The next week, Nina and Ronin still buzzed with residual excitement from their secret adventure at the Capitol as they walked into Mr. Johansson's class. Nina, with her mint backpack, made a point to show Ronin the glistening treasure pinned to her bag.

"You still have that crab brooch?" Ronin inquired.

"Of course I do! This is like the most special and important thing I have been gifted in my entire life! I would never lose it!" Nina retorted, slightly offended that Ronin would ever doubt her abilities.

As Nina carefully set down her backpack while Ronin took his seat, Mr. Johansson's commanding voice caught their attention.

"Nina and Ronin, may I see you out in the hall for a moment?"

They looked at each other with confused faces as they stood up from their desk to follow. Nina and Ronin never got called into the hallway, that's only reserved for the kids who misbehave or the kids who deserve special praise - but more often the former.

"Do you think he knows about what happened with Congresswoman Akumu?" Nina whispered, sounding slightly panicked.

"No, he can't know! How would he know?!" Ronin whispered back anxiously. They spoke with a fast beat and walked at a slow pace, trying to exchange as many words as possible before facing their teacher.

"What do you think he's calling us out into the hallway for then?"

"Maybe it's because he really likes the drawings I did for the assignment from our field trip or he wants to secretly tell me that I'm his favorite student." Ronin smirked.

"Ronin, why would he call me out for that too?" Nina gave him that 'be serious for just a few seconds' look that she got to practice so often. "Do you think Congresswoman Akumu --" She stopped talking as Mr. Johansson motioned for them to hurry up.

Their sneakered feet met the speckled floor of the hall as they both looked up to face Mr. Johansson. There was silence for a few moments and the suspense grew taller than the Capitol.

"I know what you two did," he said sternly.

Nina and Ronin whipped their heads to each other, both fearful of the consequences.

"What did we do?" Nina asked with the most innocent, goody-two-shoes voice that she could muster.

He addressed both of them. "Oh kids, I know everything - from the crab brooch to the seatbelts to bursting into rooms you aren't supposed to be in." Mr. Johansson said.

Nina and Ronin fearfully turned to each other and gulped.

"Wait a second, Mr. Johansson, how did you find all of this out? We thought we snuck back into the class seamlessly?" Ronin said with odd pride, elbowing

Nina for backup. Nina, still recovering from her shock of Mr. Johansson discovering their secret, gave Ronin another one of her looks, this one suggesting that Ronin shut his mouth.

"Well, you could imagine my surprise this morning when I received this official letter from Congresswoman Akumu." He gently pulled out a crisp white envelope from his back pocket. It was labeled with the address of the U.S Capitol and marked with the Congressional Seal. Ronin and Nina's eyes immediately lit up with curious amazement, as if fireworks were exploding before their eyes. The Congresswoman had remembered them and even wrote a letter to them!

"I wondered why our district's Congresswoman would write to me when we were only briefly introduced to her on our tour. When I opened the letter I was shocked to hear that not only did you follow a Congresswoman around the Capitol, but you made a speech to an entire committee!" He sounded incredulous. "I just couldn't believe what you two had been up to when I thought you were on tour with us." He shook his head. Distressed feelings began to wash over Nina. She had never gotten in trouble before, let alone upset a teacher like this.

He continued. "I want to once again emphasize how important it is to stay with the group on a field trip, follow directions and all that or else we could all get into big trouble."

Nina and Ronin simultaneously looked down at their feet to avoid the gaze of their assertive teacher, leaving silence to linger in the air.

Tears began to well up in Nina's eyes, but before they got the chance to flow out, Mr. Johansson added, in a lighter tone with a sigh of relief, "Now that I've gotten that out of the way, I want to say how incredibly proud I am of both of you."

Immediately, Nina and Ronin's heads shot up in utter disbelief of what their teacher just said.

"Proud?" Nina's voice quivered, not yet recovered from the tense moment before.

"Yes, proud. According to Congresswoman Akumu, you two were quite the helpers with passing that seatbelt proposal!"

"She said that? Like those words exactly?" Nina asked eagerly, scooting her feet towards Mr. Johansson.

Their teacher chuckled, "Yeah, pretty much those words, plus some exciting news. Here would you like me to read it out loud exactly how she wrote it?"

Both kids nodded their heads up and down with vigorous speed.

"Ok then, here we go:

Dear Mr. Johansson,

I am writing to congratulate you on how bright and wonderful your two students, Nina and Ronin, are. You should be so proud of how they conducted themselves on your trip to the Capitol. You may or may not have found out by now that it did not go for them as you had planned...

"She tells me about your excursion here, so I'll just skip to the good parts"

...Your kids were able to speak eloquently when they faced a group of adults (who even I think can be scary sometimes) and convinced some of my fellow members of Congress that

seatbelts should be put on school buses, which was an issue that they felt very passionate about.

Speaking of the issue, I think that they will be very happy to know that their efforts in front of the committee were not in vain and H.B.107, the Public Transportation Safety Act, passed in both the House and the Senate AND got approval from the President, thereby making it a law! I truly believe that Nina and Ronin played a big part in this and should celebrate the victory. In honor of this, my colleagues and I have ceremonially nicknamed it, 'Nina and Ronin's Law' which we hope will stick.

Your students have brave, curious, and resourceful minds and I see success in whatever they might pursue in the future. Although, I hope for Nina that her future involves a career in politics. I am happy to be a mentor for them and would, of course, be happy to answer any of their questions about the process now that the bill has passed.

Your friend,

Congresswoman Akumu

U.S. House of Representatives of Maryland's 3rd Congressional District

After Mr. Johansson concluded reading the letter, he looked at Nina and Ronin to find their jaws nearly on the floor.

"It passed??" Nina exclaimed, still processing what news she just learned, "It passed!!!"

"And it's named after us!!" Ronin added.

"Well, it's not officially named that, Ronin, but the Congresswoman does appreciate your contribution to getting the bill passed! So that's worth celebrating!" Mr. Johansson replied.

"Yayayayayayay!" Ronin and Nina shouted in unison while clasping hands and jumping up and down.

Laughing at the kids' explosion of joy, Mr. Johansson said, "Ok, ok you two, let's get back into the classroom so I can do my job and teach you something about social studies!"

The three of them reentered the classroom with Nina leading, skipping gleefully without a worry in her mind and Ronin moon-walking backwards into the classroom.

As Mr. Johansson motioned for the class to calm down, he instructed them to turn to page 269 in their textbooks. Nina however began to stare off into space and dream about what her life would be like as a Congresswoman. Like Congresswoman Akumu, she would be kind and fair, listening to everyone, especially kids. Nina saw herself commanding the attention of a committee, no, commanding the attention of the entire Congress! Nina pictured herself speaking to constituents and drafting legislation when suddenly she was pulled out of her daydream by a light cough.

"Even future Congresswomen have to read the chapter, Nina," Mr. Johansson said in a low voice with a smile.

Nina smiled brightly back and opened her book, excited to work hard towards her future.

Glossary

Congressional District (pg 18) — noun

a territorial division of states where a member of the U.S. House of Representatives is elected to represent those residing there.

Crustacean (pg 19) — noun

creatures that live in water, and normally have a soft body covered with a hard outer shell. Some examples include crabs, lobsters, and shrimps.

Committee (pg 19) — noun

(in politics) a group of people tasked to investigate, take action, or report on a particular issue

Crypt (pg 21) — noun

an underground space typically used as a chapel or burial place. Originally the crypt in the Capitol was intended to be George Washington's burial site but now it contains 13 statues from the National Statuary Hall Collection and a case where a replica of the Magna Carta was once displayed.

Spires (pg 21) — noun

tall, slim, pointed roofs on buildings, typically churches.

Estate (pg 21) — noun

an area of land that is owned by an individual or a family.

Chastise (pg 21) — verb

to scold or reprimand someone.

Foreign Affairs (pg 31) — noun

happenings abroad that affect/involve the country you live in.

Subcommittee (pg 31) — noun

a group of people from within a committee tasked with a specific problem the committee deals with.

Constituent (pg 33) — noun

a person who lives in the district that a politician represents. For instance, Congresswomen Akumu represents Nina, Ronin, and their class because they all reside in the district she oversees.

Legislation (pg 37) — noun

a law or a set of laws.

Policy (pg 37) — noun

    a set of guidelines placed by the government regarding a specific issue. These
    guidelines are generally used to ensure the safety and wellbeing of the
    community.

Immigration (pg 42) — noun

    the act of moving to permanently live in a foreign country

Bipartisanship (pg 45) — noun

    an agreement or compromise between two, normally opposing, political
    parties.

Two-party system (pg 45) — noun

    A two-party system is one in which there are only two significant political
    parties that consistently control the political scene. For instance in the U.S.
    the two party system consists of the Democratic and Republican parties.

Appropriations Committee (pg 45) — noun

    is responsible for giving and budgeting funds for most of the spending of the
    government.

Allot (pg 45) — verb

    to set aside a portion of resources, whether that be time, money, or some
    other object.

Abstain (pg 45) — verb

when a member who is allowed to vote, chooses not to vote either for or against the proposal.

Veto (pg 46) — Noun

the power of the president to stop a bill passed by Congress from becoming law.

National Statuary Hall Collection (pg 48) — noun

a collection of statues in the US Capitol donated by individual states to honor notable people in each state's history. Currently the collection now consists of 100 statues contributed by 50 states as well as newly commissioned statues from recent presidents.

Continental Congress (pg 49) — noun

a group of representatives from each state that met during the American Revolution to draft the Declaration of Independence, provided leadership during the American Revolution, and authored both the Articles of Confederation and the Constitution.

Articles of Confederation (pg 49) — noun

were the United States' first Constitution directly after the American Revolution. The document was in effect from 1781 until 1787 and established the laws of the 13 independent American colonies.

U.S. Constitution (pg 49) — noun

the document that outlines the basic foundations, laws, and structure of the United States government.

Supreme Court (pg 53) — noun

the most powerful federal court of the United States. The Court's job is to interpret the meaning of a law, decide whether it is constitutional, and rule on how the law should be applied.

Ideological (pg 54) — adjective

A set of ideas that government or political parties follow. For instance the U.S government follows the ideology of democracy.

Residual (pg 59) — adjective

the last few remains of an object or feeling.

Eloquently (pg 62) — adjective

being able to communicate effectively and gracefully

Drafting Legislation (pg 64) — verb

to write legislation, also know as laws.

Acknowledgements

"I think realizing that you're not alone, that you are standing with millions of your sisters around the world is vital"

Malala Yousafzai

Every magazine we publish, every student we reach, and now every book we publish, the work our team does never ceases to amaze us.

And behind every Women In Politics milestone is a whole family of supporters, and this book couldn't have had a better family fighting for it every step of the way.

First off, a huge thanks to our inimitable team, whose passion, determination, and talents have made this book and organization a beautiful gift. We are forever grateful to be working alongside such powerful women, who not only inspire our community but continue to inspire us every single day.

Thank you also to all the teachers who have put their heart and time into being the fiercest editors: John Flagger, Julianna Freed, Lisa Levinthal, Heather Espana, China Harvey, and Jami Greer, thank you for all the work you have put into this book. Without your support, time, and dedication this book would not be able to touch all these hearts.

There are so many other Women In Politics team members who have been essential to Little Lawmaker's publication, but we especially need to thank: Andrea Montenegro, for not only being our layout designer but also never failing to make us laugh even in the more difficult phases of making this book. We also want to thank Cedar Roach, Kaylyn Allingham, Lila Rowland, Lily Mott, Nuha Khan, Regan Madding, Sarah Han, Sophia Escobar, and Talia Zafari for being amazing editors who helped shape Little Lawmakers from its beginning stage to now.

We also want to thank our devoted graphic designer: Anoushka Sharma thank you for the time and effort you put into bringing these characters to life.

And last, but certainly, not least we want to thank our dedicated writers: Ella Stillion Southard, Ting Cui, Hanna Matsukawa, and Nithan Rajappa you four have been through the Little Lawmakers journey since the inception of the idea, all the way to watching Little Lawmakers come into fruition. The four of you have spent months alongside both of us writing this book, and your dedication and passion have made this book special to everyone who reads it.

And of course, thank you to all our families, friends, and supporters for being the biggest cheerleaders we could have ever asked for. Your continued encouragement and love are our driving force.

With much love,
Rebecca Joseph and Katherine Bronov
Co-Executives of Women In Politics

About Women In Politics

Women In Politics was founded in May 2020, by Rebecca Joseph, in the midst of the COVID-19 pandemic, and the team grew worldwide shortly after a viral TikTok video. With over 150 team members WIP strives to ensure that politics is a tangible career path for young women through our magazine and community outreach: state chapters, social media, and community Geneva. Together, at Women In Politics, we are fostering a community of girls across the world passionate about politics.

Connect with us!

🌐 https://womeninpolitics.co/

♪ @womeninpoliticsss

📷 @womeninpolitics_

About the Creators

Rebecca Joseph and Katherine Bronov
Co-Executive Directors of Women In Politics

Rebecca Joseph is a 16 years old high school senior from San Francisco, California. She is the founder and co-executive of Women In Politics along with her co-executive Katherine Bronov. Katherine is a 19-year-old college student from the suburbs of Philadelphia, Pennsylvania studying political science at American University in Washington D.C. Both Rebecca and Katherine are passionate about politics and the engagement of young people, particularly women such as themselves in the political process in the US and around the world. Women In Politics and its leadership believe that it is never too early to get involved and we hope that through this book, other kids will feel empowered to use their voices and can find their love for politics.

Anoushka Sharma
Illustrator

Anoushka Sharma is a self-taught digital illustrator, creator, and community worker. She attended the University of California, Davis, where she studied Neurobiology, Physiology, & Behavior. Her pieces are greatly inspired by her upbringing as a Nepalese American, as well as her passion for equity and healthcare. She hopes readers of all ages will find inspiration through this story and its characters to pursue their dreams of all kinds! This is her first children's book.

Ella Stillion Southard
Co-Author

Ella Stillion Southard is an 18-year-old student from Athens, Georgia studying at John Cabot University in Rome, Italy. She is a magazine leader on the Women In Politics team and has been a part of the organization since its founding in May 2020. She hopes that from this book, kids, as well as older readers, will understand that there is a pace for them to follow their dreams, whether that's in politics or not.

Ting Cui
Co-Author

Ting Cui is a 19-year-old college student from the suburbs of Baltimore, Maryland, studying at Middlebury College. She is a magazine writer on the Women In Politics team and has been a part of the organization since 2020. Ting started writing for Women In Politics because she wanted to be a part of a community of ambitious young women with a passion for politics. She has had a blast meeting such intelligent ladies throughout the process of creating the book, and cannot wait to see the impact the book has.

Nithan Rajappa
Co-Author

Nithan Rajappa is a 17-year-old student from Santa Barbara, California, who will be studying journalism at Northwestern University in Evanston, Illinois. They have been a staff writer for the Women In Politics magazine since January 2021. They hope that everyone who reads this book feels seen and empowered like someone believes in their potential and is ready to see them fulfill it.

Hanna Matsukawa
Co-Author

Hanna Matsukawa is a 19-year-old college student from Philadelphia, Pennsylvania, studying at Wellesley College. She is a magazine writer on the Women In Politics team and has been a part of the organization since 2020. Hanna had a wonderful time working on Little Lawmakers with such an amazing team and hopes Little Lawmakers inspires children, especially young girls, to engage in politics and create a more diverse and equitable society.

Made in the USA
Las Vegas, NV
25 August 2022

54036907R00046